Invention No.8 in F Major
BWV779

Composed by Johann Sebastian Bach

CLASSICAL
PIANO SOLOS
COLLECTION

VOLUME *FOUR*

Wise Publications
London/New York/Paris/Sydney/Copenhagen/Madrid

Exclusive Distributors:

Music Sales Limited
8/9 Frith Street, London W1V 5TZ, England.

Music Sales Pty Limited
120 Rothschild Avenue, Rosebery, NSW 2018, Australia.

Music Sales Corporation
257 Park Avenue South, New York, NY10010, United States of America.

Order No. AM91537
ISBN 0-7119-3759-1
This book © Copyright 1994 by Wise Publications

Book design by Studio Twenty, London
Computer management by Adam Hay Editorial Design
Compiled by Stephen Harding

YOUR GUARANTEE OF QUALITY
As publishers, we strive to produce every book to the highest commercial standards.
This book has been carefully designed to minimise awkward page turns and to make
playing from it a real pleasure.
Particular care has been given to specifying acid-free, neutral-sized paper made from pulps
which have not been elemental chlorine bleached. This pulp is from farmed sustainable forests
and was produced with special regard for the environment.
Throughout, the printing and binding have been planned to ensure a sturdy,
attractive publication which should give years of enjoyment.
If your copy fails to meet our high standards, please inform us and
we will gladly replace it.

Music Sales' complete catalogue describes thousands of titles and
is available in full colour sections by subject, direct from Music Sales Limited.
Please state your areas of interest and send a cheque/postal order for £1.50 for postage to:
Music Sales Limited, Newmarket Road, Bury St. Edmunds, Suffolk IP33 3YB.

5

Bagatelle in A major
Op.33, No.4

Composed by Ludwig van Beethoven

Piano Sonata No.9 in E Major
Op.14, No.1 - 2nd Movement

Composed by Ludwig van Beethoven

Allegretto

Maggiore

[legato]

Allegretto da capo
sin' al Maggiore,
e poi la Coda.

Coda

9

Intermezzo in B♭ Minor
Op.117, No.2

Composed by Johannes Brahms

Andante non troppo e con molta espressione

11

13

Canon

Composed by César Franck

Poco allegretto

Mazurka in B♭ Major
Op.7, No.1

Composed by Frédéric Chopin

Humoresque
Op.101, No.7

Composed by Antonin Dvořák

Bell Ringing
Op.54, No.6

Composed by Edvard Grieg

23

Allegro
from Suite No.7

Composed by George Frideric Handel

Piano Sonata in E♭ Major
Hob.XVI:49 - 1st Movement

Composed by Joseph Haydn

Prelude in E Minor
Op.11, No.4

Composed by Alexander Scriabin

Nuages Gris

Composed by Franz Liszt

(poco a poco agitato)

sempre legato
ped. simile)

(calmando)

rall.
p

35

Piano Sonata in G
K283 - 1st Movement
Composed by Wolfgang Amadeus Mozart

Allegro

37

Mouvement Perpetuel No. 1

Composed by Francis Poulenc

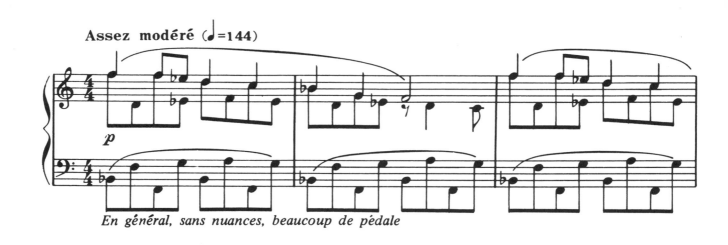

En général, sans nuances, beaucoup de pédale

incolore et toujours ***p***

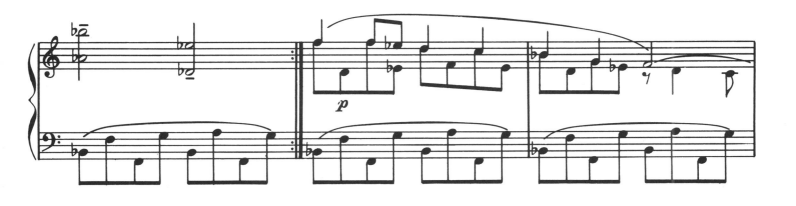

p

ralentir en pesant sur la main droite

Très lent

8va

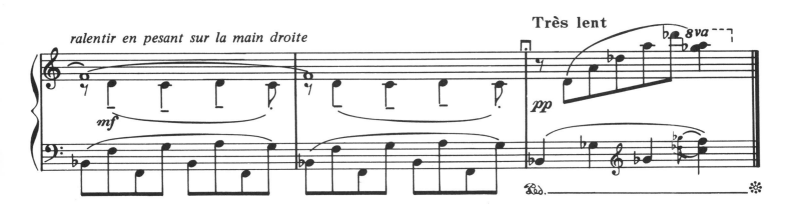

mf

pp

41

Impromptu in A♭
Op.142/D.935, No.2

Composed by Franz Schubert

Printed and bound in Great Britain by
Caligraving Limited Thetford Norfolk

10/97(29013)

Feuillet d'Album
Op.19, No.3

Composed by Peter Ilyich Tchaikovsky

Allegretto semplice

Of Foreign Lands And People - No.1
from Scenes Of Childhood

Composed by Robert Schumann